SAMSPIRATION

By Samuel Jacobs

Samspiration
Printed in the United States
© Copyright 2018, by Samuel Jacobs
Illustrated by Sadiqa Akhter
Cover illustration original photo by Joe Hesch

ISBN: 978-0-9981817-1-4
Library of Congress Control Number: 2018908072

Published by Bukola Oriola Group, LLC formerly known as Bukola Braiding & Beauty Supply, LLC
2612 Cutters Grove Ave #305
Anoka MN 55303

Email: info@bukolaoriola.com

I dedicate this book to all my teachers from pre-school at Head Start - ACCAP, Coon Rapids, to Lincoln Elementary School For the Arts, Anoka, Minnesota.

This book is about my artwork from school and home. It shows that you can can do anything, if you put your mind to it. I also shared some personal experiences on canoeing, fishing, and my travel to Nigeria.

My Self Portrait

Watercolor Landscape

My Watercolor Landscape artwork received a ribbon for being selected as an artwork for dispaly at the Banfill-Locke Art Gallery in Fridley, Minnesota.

Contour Line Leaf Drawing

Leaf Print

Goofy at the beach in Lagos.

Art is creative

You never know what you can do unless you try.

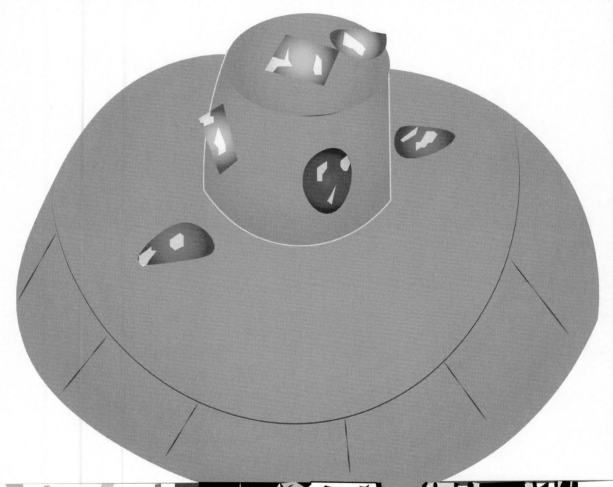

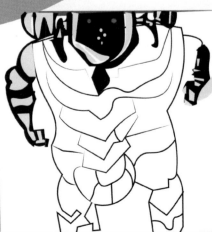

Pop Art Sandwich

Pop Art Ice Cream

Textured Landscape

Trying new things can be fun.

Colorwheel Birch Trees

The raccoons that stole the Christmas decorations

Impressionist Seascape

Do something you like to do.

Blue Ninja

Do not let negative thoughts overcome you.
Think positive.

Ojibwe and Dakota Design Prints

The Ojibwe and Dakota Tribes are Native American Tribes in the United States.

Georgia O'Keeffe

Mountainous Sunrise

Mountainous Sunrise
By : Samuel Jacobs

The blueish mountains in the distance.
Standing with their pride.
As it gets lighter and farther, the fresh smelling air
fills my lungs.

The Greenish blue sky up so high.
Making the sunrise better.
As I feel the wind, I get tired.

Fishing

I went fishing with my friend, Uncle Joe, at a pond in Coon Rapids, Minnesota when I was five years old.

My first trip to Nigeria. I had a stop over in Amsterdam, Netherlands.

I had French fries and chicken at the airport.

Fun at Shoprite mall, Lagos, Nigeria.

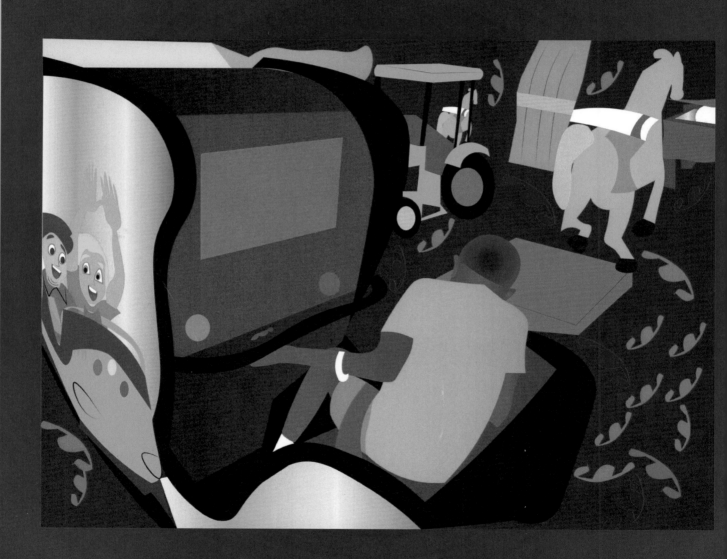

Fishing and canoe tipping story

In 2011 when I was five years old, I went fishing with a friend named Uncle Joe. I was in pre-school at the time at Head Start.

When we were on the lake, a speed boat went fast across the water that caused big waves. The waves hit us and we got tipped over in our canoe.

We lost some stuff because they sank, but we retrieved some. Two other people came over in their speed boat to help us out. They came over to us and the first thing they did was lift me into their boat, then they had some rope that Uncle Joe grabbed. They slowly sailed to the shore to get us to safety.

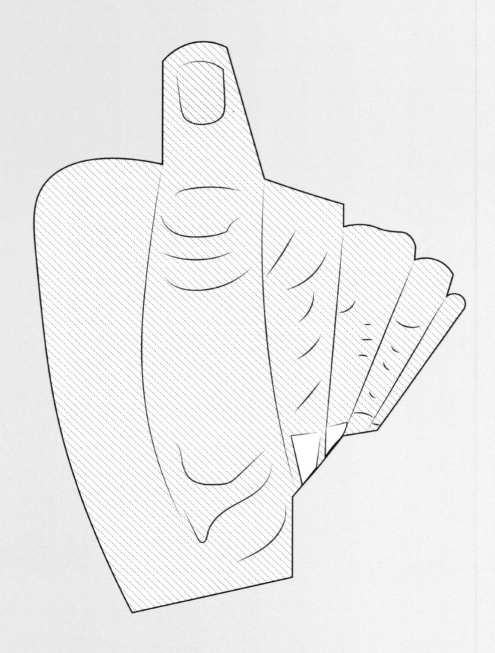

Japanese Cherry Blossoms

Share a place you have traveled or will like to travel to. Ask your mom, dad, aunt, uncle or teacher to share it on my Facebook page, Samspiration.

Made in the USA
Columbia, SC
05 November 2018